## DEDICATION

To my wife, Surenity Blitz, Dawn Lee McMahon-Trites, and all those who work tirelessly to help support the Saint Bernard Rescue Network, founded by Dawn, to provide homes, medical care, food, and love to these gentle giants.

For Wilson, Yodel, Sasha, Lady, and Trouble—with whom I have had some of the best adventures!

www.mascotbooks.com

*A Dog Named Trouble...Goes to a Forever Home*

**For more information, please contact:**
Mascot Books
620 Herndon Parkway, Suite 320
Herndon, VA 20170
info@mascotbooks.com

Library of Congress Control Number: 2020915168

CPSIA Code: PRT1220A

ISBN-13: 978-1-64543-600-3

Printed in the United States

# A Dog Named
# TROUBLE
## ...Goes to a Forever Home

**Anthony Gonzalez**
Illustrated by Walter Policelli

## When you rescue a pet, sometimes you start to wonder who got rescued...

In December of 2018, my wife and I saw an online post from the Saint Bernard Rescue Network out of Pennsylvania for a Saint who was in a shelter in Maryland. The pup was seven years old and had spent the majority of his life in a kennel. Shelters have limited resources, so large breeds with their appetites and strength don't always do well in shelters, and often need to be put in foster homes or adopted shortly after they arrive to give them a healthy environment to live in.

My wife and I went to pick up the pup, whose name was Charlie, but he never responded to that name. We commented to him one day that he was in trouble for breaking furniture and he responded to "trouble," so "TROUBLE" became his new name! He is our fourth Saint Bernard rescue: rambunctious, fun, always smiling, smart, and with a huge appetite, he manages to earn his name every single day.

Each rescue pet comes with a different past, and when you start the journey with them, their transition into the family can take days, weeks, or even months before they are comfortable in their new surroundings. A rescue pet doesn't necessarily have issues—they just need time to adjust to a loving and understanding home. Trouble took weeks to adjust, but since he is so smart, he was quick to test the waters for his limits at every opportunity. His antics were the inspiration for this book. It has been two years now since Trouble became part of our family. He is still learning new things, finding things that he enjoys, and driving his Mommy crazy sometimes, but we love him.

Trouble is a seven-year-old Saint Bernard who lives in a shelter. He weighs 195 pounds and always has a smile on his face. Today, he meets his new family.

When Trouble first met his new family, he was nervous and confused. He sniffed his new owners, and loved to be cuddled and hugged by his new Mommy, but was cautious at first with his new Daddy.

Trouble was anxious to leave the shelter and dragged his new Daddy through the nearby field, sniffing everything he could.

When Trouble got to his new home, he explored his territory—inside the house, outside the house, all around the garden, and even under the deck. He guards his yard from the nearby fox and protects the bunny rabbits that play nearby.

The first night, Trouble's new Daddy read a book to him to calm him and make him sleepy. It worked. The gentle giant went to sleep next to his Daddy.

A CAT in the LAUNDROMAT

Trouble's Mommy got him two new blankets. One was a blue felt blanket and the other was a "Mr. Owl" blanket. He loved his new blankets and made a little bed out of them.

The next day, Trouble discovered how wonderful it was to play with the children from next door, and he decided that he loved children. Later that day, the big pup took a ride in his Daddy's truck and was so excited to feel the wind on his face.

Trouble's favorite rides end at the hamburger stand. He gets excited and nudges Daddy when they are close to the burger stand because he knows Daddy will get him four burgers.

Trouble discovered how much he loves the taste of rain water. So, he carried buckets in the yard to try to catch the rain like he sees Daddy do for him.

In the house, Trouble has his eye on the couch—it is much softer than the floor. Mommy tells him he is not allowed on the couch. But Trouble decides to just try sitting for a second.

Trouble also thinks he is a lap dog. When Daddy sits on the floor, the big guy will go to sit on his lap without fail.

Trouble learned that he gets more rides when he brings his leash to Daddy and walks himself to the truck.

Trouble enjoys having a pound of meat mixed in with his dog food.

He prefers brisket, but will gladly take chicken, beef, turkey, or tuna.

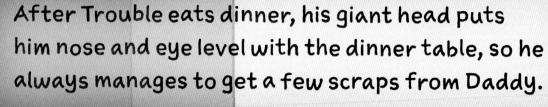

After Trouble eats dinner, his giant head puts him nose and eye level with the dinner table, so he always manages to get a few scraps from Daddy.

Trouble visits his friends at doggie daycare often. He is an alpha male, so he acts like daycare is his kingdom. He is huge compared to the other dogs, so he gets respect. Trouble likes that.

Daddy went to sit with Trouble after daycare and they waited for Mommy to bring the bigger truck. But when Daddy opened the door to his little truck, Trouble was not going to miss the opportunity for a ride, so he wedged himself into Daddy's truck.

How do you get a 195-pound dog out of a little truck? Daddy thought...aha!...hamburgers! So, Daddy stopped by the burger stand on the way home to round up some burgers to convince the giant Saint to get out of the truck.

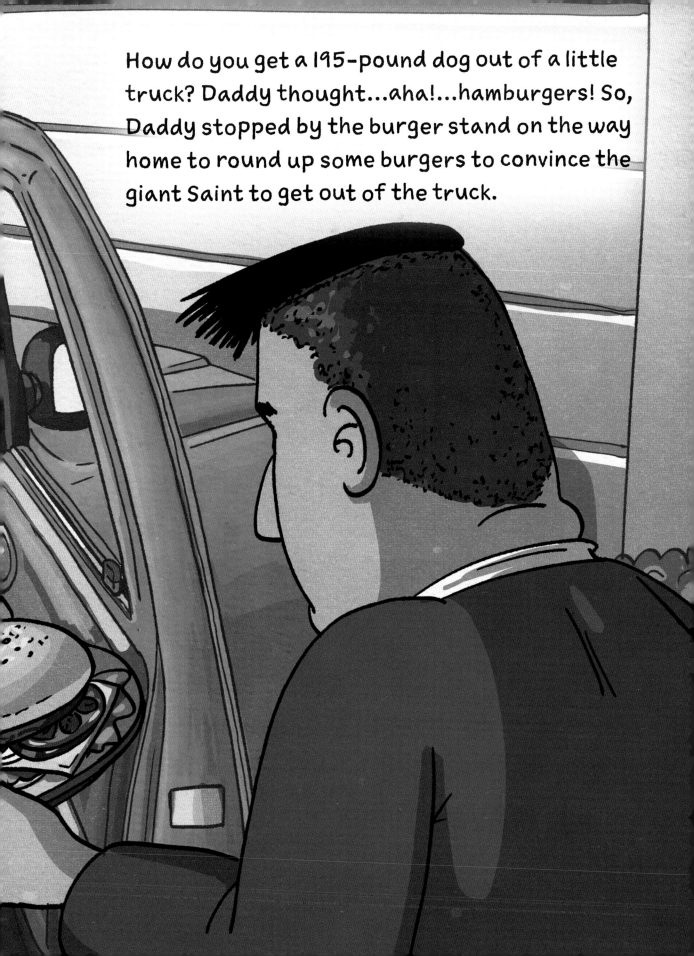

Trouble does not like laundry day. When Mommy grabs his blanket, he stares at her while she picks it up.

When Mommy is not looking, Trouble grabs his blanket and runs into the backyard to try to hide it under the deck.

Trouble loves to play tug-of-war against Daddy with his rope toy. He will swing his head, violently growling and then running with his toy while dragging Daddy around the yard. Trouble is a tug-of-war champion!

Trouble loves to get a bath. But first, he makes Daddy chase him around the yard. Trouble wants to make sure he gets extra dirty before he gets his bath.

Trouble loves to be brushed, and falls asleep afterwards at the foot of the bed with his blue blanket.

But, Trouble does not like complete darkness, so Daddy found a night light to help him sleep.

# Meet the real

# TROUBLE!

## ABOUT THE AUTHOR

Anthony Gonzalez was born in Houston, Texas, and after earning a degree from the US Naval Academy, he completed a twenty-four-year military career. He currently resides in Fredericksburg, Virginia, with his wife, Surenity Blitz, and their Saint Bernard, Trouble. Anthony and his wife have been involved with the Saint Bernard Rescue Network since 2011 and they continue to open their home and hearts to Saints in need. Anthony's inspiration for writing the book came from his co-worker, Andrew, who suggested that he write a children's book after looking at pictures of Trouble's antics. Anthony had kept a journal and pictures to remind him of the funny and crazy things his dog had a knack for doing, so writing about Trouble was fun and relaxing.

f  Saint Bernard Rescue Network